King Midas's Golden Touch

By Julia Jarman
Illustrated by Claudia Venturini

FRANKLIN WATTS
LONDON•SYDNEY

First published in 2009 by
Franklin Watts
338 Euston Road
London
NW1 3BH

Franklin Watts Australia
Level 17/207 Kent Street
Sydney
NSW 2000

A CIP catalogue record for this book is available
from the British Library.

ISBN 978 0 7496 8585 0 (hbk)
ISBN 978 0 7496 8589 8 (pbk)

Series Editor: Melanie Palmer
Series Advisor: Dr Barrie Wade
Series Designer: Peter Scoulding

Printed in China

Franklin Watts is a division of
Hachette Children's Books,
an Hachette UK company
www.hachette.co.uk

Long ago in a land called Phrygia,
there lived a king called Midas.

He was rich and kind,
but sometimes very foolish.

He lived in a splendid palace with his daughter, Zoe. He loved her dearly, even more than his famous rose garden.

Every morning they walked in the garden, stopping to admire the lovely roses and breathe in their delicious scent.

One morning they found a strange
creature, half-man and half-goat,
sleeping under one of the bushes.

"What is *that*?" Zoe asked.

Her father smiled,

"It is the old satyr, Silenus."

"You drank too much wine last night, Silenus," said the king. The satyr woke up, groaning.

As they helped him to his feet,
Midas told Zoe that Silenus was
a friend of Dionysus, god of wine.
Then suddenly ...

... there was a flash of lightning and a cloud of smoke!

And out of the smoke appeared
the god himself, Dionysus.

"Midas, thank you for looking after my old friend," he boomed. "Wish for anything you like and I will grant it. That is my reward to you."

12

"Anything?" said Midas.

"Yes, anything," said the god.

"I wish for everything I touch to turn to gold," said Midas, quickly. "Are you sure?" boomed Dionysus. "Think about it first."

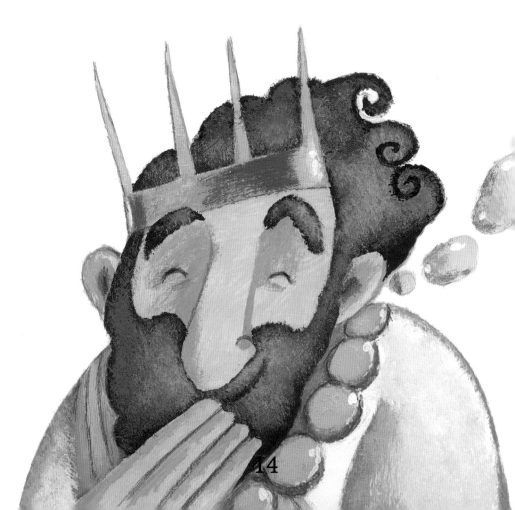

14

But Midas didn't want to think.
He just wanted to be the richest
man in the world.

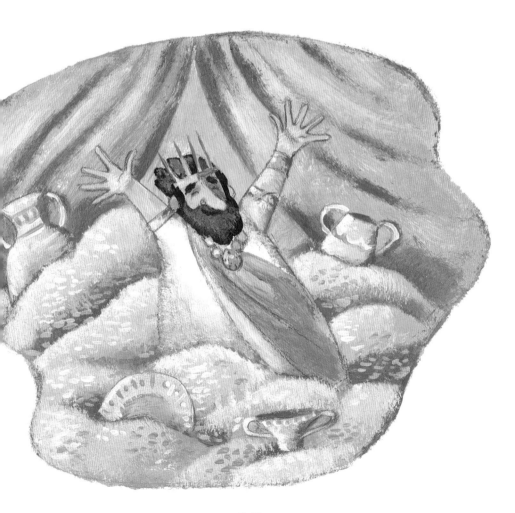

So the god granted his wish –
and the king's troubles began.

At first, King Midas was delighted.
He touched a table ...

and it turned to gold.

He touched one of his

lovely roses ...

and they all turned to gold.

"This is wonderful!" Midas cried.
When he put his hand in the
fountain, the water turned to gold.

Joyfully, he went to dinner and tried to eat, but the food turned to gold.

He tried to drink, but the wine
turned to gold.

"Father, what have you done?"
cried Zoe, putting her arms
around him and ...

she turned to gold!

Now shame and sadness
filled the king's heart.
"Dionysus, please undo the
wish," he begged.

But the god just said,
"Go to the river and cover
yourself with water."

King Midas thought about it.
What if *he* turned to gold? But
then he thought about Zoe. Life
without her was not worth living.

He rushed to the river, clutching her golden body, and plunged into the water!

He didn't turn to gold. Nor did
the water. Best of all, his beloved
daughter came back to life.
His golden touch had gone!

But even now, people say that the water in that faraway river has a golden gleam.

29

Puzzle 1

Put these pictures in the correct order.

Which event do you think is most important?

Now try writing the story in your own words!

Puzzle 2

Choose the correct speech bubbles for each character. Can you think of any others?
Turn over to find the answers.

Answers

Puzzle 1

The correct order is

1d, 2f, 3a, 4e, 5c, 6b

Puzzle 2

King Midas: 3, 4

Zoe: 1, 6

Dionysus: 2, 5

Look out for more Hopscotch Myths:

Icarus, the Boy Who Flew
ISBN 978 0 7496 7992 7*
ISBN 978 0 7496 8000 8

**Perseus and the
Snake Monster**
ISBN 978 0 7496 7993 4*
ISBN 978 0 7496 8001 5

**Odysseus and the
Wooden Horse**
ISBN 978 0 7496 7994 1*
ISBN 978 0 7496 8002 2

**Persephone and the
Pomegranate Seeds**
ISBN 978 0 7496 7995 8*
ISBN 978 0 7496 8003 9

Romulus and Remus
ISBN 978 0 7496 7996 5*
ISBN 978 0 7496 8004 6

Thor's Hammer
ISBN 978 0 7496 7997 2*
ISBN 978 0 7496 8005 3

Gelert the Brave
ISBN 978 0 7496 7999 6*
ISBN 978 0 7496 8007 7

No Dinner for Anansi
ISBN 978 0 7496 8006 0

King Midas's Golden Touch
ISBN 978 0 7496 8585 0*
ISBN 978 0 7496 8589 8

**Theseus and the
Minotaur**
ISBN 978 0 7496 8586 7*
ISBN 978 0 7496 8590 4

**Jason's Quest for the
Golden Fleece**
ISBN 978 0 7496 8587 4*
ISBN 978 0 7496 8591 1

**Heracles and the
Terrible Tasks**
ISBN 978 0 7496 8588 1*
ISBN 978 0 7496 8592 8

For more Hopscotch books go to: www.franklinwatts.co.uk

* hardback